This Annual belongs to

_____

Published 2021
Little Brother Books Ltd, Ground Floor, 23 Southernhay East, Exeter, Devon, EX1 1QL
Printed in Poland. ul. Połczyńska 99,01 303 Warszawa.
books@littlebrotherbooks.co.uk
www.littlebrotherbooks.co.uk
Images used under license from Shutterstock.

Contents

Welcome to CoComelon

Hi, its great to see you!

Do you love to sing, dance and find out about the world?

Then CoComelon is just the place for you.

Let's say hello to all the new friends you're about to meet!

YoYo

JJ

TomTom

My name is YoYo and I am brave.

Hi, I'm JJ and I love to sing!

I'm TomTom and I love to build things!

Nico

Well hello there! My name is Nico and I love to sing LOUD!

Nina

Pleased to meet you! I'm Nina and I love to have fun.

Cody

Hey, Cody here! My favourite thing in the world is dinosaurs. ROAR!

CeCe

Hello you! I'm called CeCe and I just love to perform.

Bella

I'm Bella, it's good to see you. You'll always find me reading a book.

Are you ready for some fun? Turn the page and let's begin, CoComelon style!

The Playdate Song!

Let's Sing

🎵 It's better to work together,

What do you like to play when a friend comes around?

Because it's double the fun.

I have fun when you have fun,

Share when you only have one!

When we work together, everyone has more fun!

Time to play

JJ loves to meet his friends at nursery!

Can you spot 3 differences between the two pictures?

Draw a big tick each time you spot something.

You did it!

What colour are JJ's shorts? Colour this box the same colour!

Trace over the letters to see what YoYo likes to do

play

Is TomTom in the second picture?

Yes

No

Look really closely!

Answers on pages 76-77

Perfect puzzle

It's great to take a day at the beach!

Draw lines to fit the pieces back into this seaside puzzle.

What's your favourite flavour of ice cream?

Answers on pages 76-77

On the Move

Vroom! Let's join JJ for some colouring fun.

Colour some bright clothes for JJ.

Colour this truck red

Colour this bus yellow

Finished? Zoom around the room like you're in a truck!

13

I can See...

What a fun day out at the beach!

The friends love paddling and splashing in the water.

Cody is hiding somewhere, Shout, 'Found you!' when you spot him.

Can you find:

 **Bucket**

  Spade

 Sun

Happy Sunny Day!

What's your favourite thing about the seaside?

Answers on pages 76-77

Ice lolly

Kite

Sandcastle

Scrub, Scrub, Scrub!

Nina knows that looking after your teeth gives you the brightest smile.

What colour toothbrush would you like?

Now let's squeeze on some toothpaste! Add **red** and **blue** scribbles.

Colour in with your favourite colour.

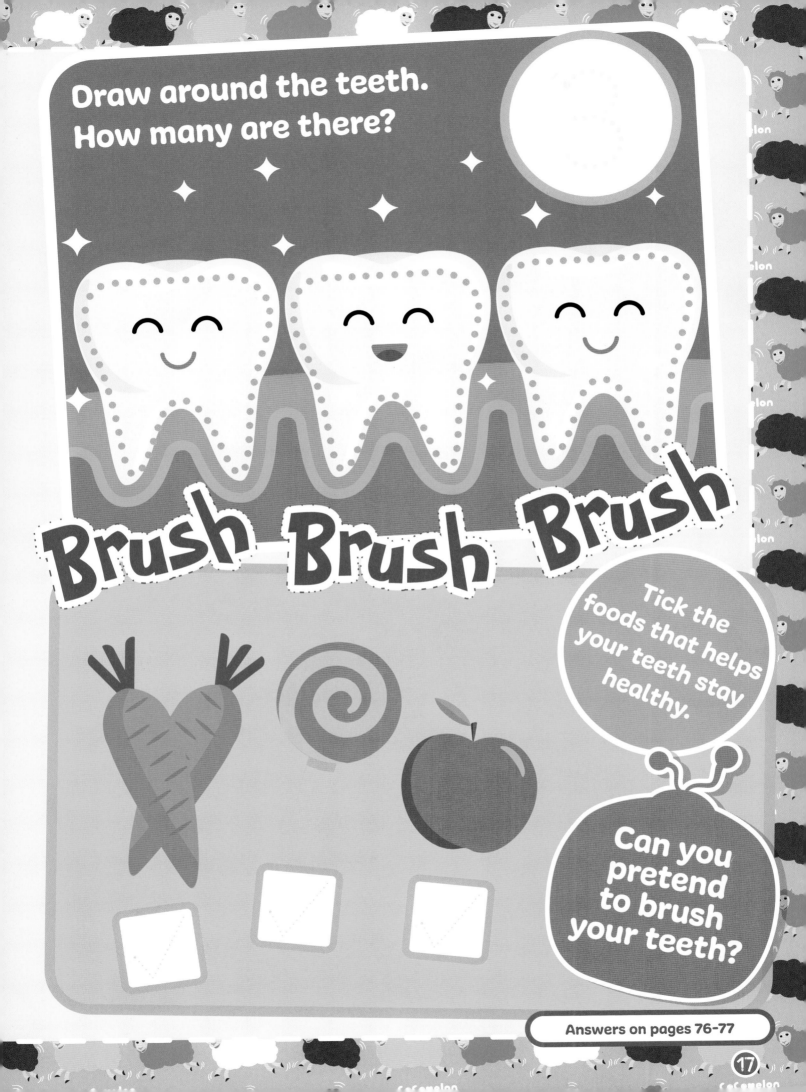

Draw around the teeth.
How many are there?

Brush Brush Brush

Tick the foods that helps your teeth stay healthy.

Can you pretend to brush your teeth?

Answers on pages 76-77

17

Pat a cake

Let's Sing

♪ Pat a cake pat a cake, baker's man,

♪ bake me a cake as fast as you can.

18

Pat it and prick it and mark with a B,

put it in the oven for baby and me!

Draw over this B on top of the cake.

I can learn... the days of the week!

Make every day special with JJ and friends.

Monday

I stayed in my bed all night.

Tuesday

I tried a new food.

Wednesday

I was kind.

It's a school day!

Join the friends on the cool school bus!

I drew a...

☐ rectangle

◯ circle

··· line

◯ octagon

☐ square

Great drawing! Now wave to all the friends on the bus!

23

Cody's having a party

You're invited, too!

Draw 3 more balloons.

Trace over the letters to see what the friends will sing to Cody.

happy birthday

CeCe is having ice cream!
Which flavour do you like best?

Cody has lost his dino stuffie! Can you find it for him?

Can you draw a yummy birthday cake here?

What do you like most about birthday parties?

Answers on pages 76-77

I can count!

Join the counting party with CeCe and Bella.

Count to 5 and colour as you go.

1
yellow star

2
red trucks

3
blue hats

26

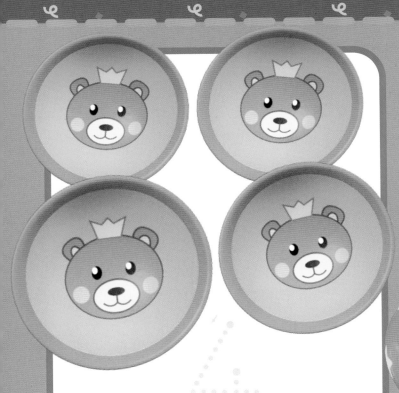

green bowls

Can you count backwards from 5 to 1?

pink balloons

The Wheels on the bus

Let's Sing

The wheels on the bus go round and round, round and round, round and round.

The wheels on the bus go round and round, all through the town.

Can you join in with these actions?

Round and round.

Swish, swish, swish.

Beep, beep, beep.

Open and shut.

Dinner Time

The CoComelon crew love to try new food.

Yes Yes Vegetables!

Follow the coloured dots to make a delicious plate of vegetables for CeCe.

Draw something you like to eat, here!

Hmm, something's not right! Can you help TomTom spot the odd animal out in each row?

Amazing animals

It's a CoComelon Pet party!

1
a b c d

2
a b c d

3
a b c d

4
a b c d

Point to the animal that's different on each row.

It's bath time

A bubbly bath is a lovely way to end the day.

2

3

5

Answers on pages 76-77

Help JJ find all the things that have fallen into the tub.

Submarine

Yacht

32

Draw 5 really big bubbles!

Colour a fluffy towel to get nice and dry.

Can you pretend to wash your face and hands? Good job!

Boat

Shark

Rubber duck

Family faces

Let's draw JJ and his siblings.

Trace over the other half of each face.

JJ

YoYo

TomTom

Draw a picture of yourself into this square!

Can you write your name here?

Yummy veggies

Grab your favourite pencils and add some colour to this scrummy picture.

Veggies help us grow up too!

Tell your grown-up what your favourite vegetable is.

The potty song!

Let's Sing

I've got the funny feeling way down low,
I've got the funny feeling, I think I have to go,

Just sit on the potty, sit and wait
Sit on the potty and it will be great!

I went to the potty! Look and see!
I went to the potty, hooray for me!

Great job, JJ, now wash your hands!

Give yourself
a big clap next time
you use the potty.

Sweet Dreams

JJ, YoYo and TomTom are ready for bed. Draw what they are all dreaming about.

ZZZ

Join the dots to find out their dream wishes.

BAA
BAA

40

ZZZ...

My family

Say 'hello' to JJ and his family!

This is JJ's dad

This is JJ's mum

This is JJ's brother
TomTom

This is
JJ

This is JJ's sister
YoYo

This is JJ's home

Draw a picture of your home here!

It's lunchtime!

Help CeCe count all the yummy things in her lunchbox.

1 apple

2 sandwiches

3 grapes

Good job!

1... 2... 3... count with me!

Join in the JJ fun and count to ten.

1 big jump

Clap your hands as loudly as you can!

2 hands to clap

3 teddies to hug

Pull your silliest face!

4 silly faces

5
cheerful cats

6
ice cream swirls

7
cute rainbows

8
bathtime ducks

9
sheep to count

Wave all 10 of your fingers at JJ now!

10
fingers to wave

Rock a bye baby

Let's Sing

Rock a bye baby, in the tree top

When the wind blows, the cradle will rock

48

When the bough breaks, the cradle will fall

And down will come baby, cradle and all

What's your favourite lullaby?

Dress up!

Make brilliant animal masks to play with JJ.

You will need:

Safety scissors

A pencil

String

Your grown-up

Make sure you've read pages 49 & 52 before you start cutting out! If you don't want to cut up your Annual, photocopy or scan and print the pages instead!

Ask a grown-up for help before using scissors.

Instructions:
1. Snip out the masks with your grown-up.
2. Push a pencil through the circles to make holes.
3. Choose a mask and tie the string to fit it around your head.

Happy sunny day!

Guide JJ and YoYo across the beach so they can get an ice lolly.

Add some yummy colour to the ice cream.

Fast colourful cars!

JJ loves his toy vehicles.

Draw lines to match each vehicle into pairs.

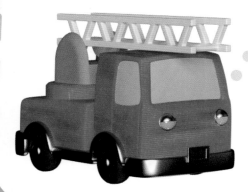

cream

Answers on pages 76-77

Vroom vroom

JJ and Kiki are ready for adventure.

Can you think of a song about buses? Sing it out loud!

Cute as a rainbow!

Can you find the right colours to help JJ finish off these words.

LEARNING is FUN!

yellow
red
blue
green

56

Happy and smart!

Cody is playing with shapes.

Draw lines from the shapes to fit them in the right holes.

What is your favourite shape? Point to it.

Reach for it

Copy JJ's family and friends moves and be a Cocomelon superstar!

Balance on one leg!

Hug your hands to your chest.

Reach both hands in the air.

Put your hands on your tummy and laugh out loud.

Make a fist and
punch the air.

Do a thumbs up!

Point in the air and
point your foot.

IT'S
PLAYTIME!

Three little pigs

Look out for the big bad wolf!

Once upon a time there were three little pigs. The time had come for them to leave home and make their fortune.

The first little pig built his house of straw, because it was the easiest thing to do. The second little pig built his house out of sticks. It was a little bit stronger than a straw house. The third little pig built his house out of bricks.

One day the big bad wolf, who loved to tease the little piggies, came along and saw the first little piggy in his house of straw. "Let me in, little piggy," he said, "or I'll huff and I'll puff and I'll blow your house in." "Not by the hairs on my chinny, chin, chin," said the first little piggy. The wolf huffed and puffed and blew his house down.

The little piggy ran as fast as he could to the house of sticks. The wolf ran after them. "Let me in, little piggies," the wolf said, "or I'll huff and I'll puff and I'll blow your house down." "Not by the hairs on my chinny, chin, chin," said the second little pig. The wolf huffed and puffed and blew his house down.

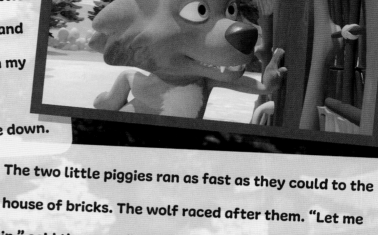

The two little piggies ran as fast as they could to the house of bricks. The wolf raced after them. "Let me in," said the wolf, "or I'll huff and I'll puff until I blow your house in!" "Not by the hairs on my chinny, chin, chin," said the third little pig. The wolf huffed and puffed but he could not blow the house down.

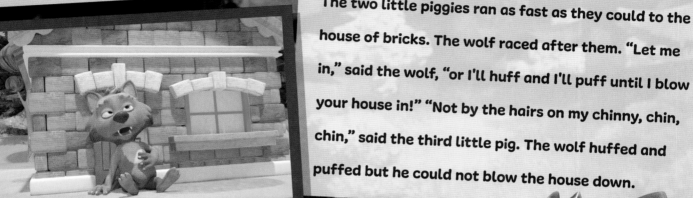

The wolf climbed onto the roof and climbed down the chimney. "I'll get you little piggies!" he said.

The third little piggy lit a roaring fire in the fireplace. "Ow! Ow! Ow!" shouted the wolf, trying to keep his feet out of the dancing flames. It was so hot that the wolf scrambled back up the chimney and ran far away into the woods, and the three little piggies lived happily ever after in the house made of bricks.

The end.

Let's all count sheep!

Nap time!

Count all the fluffy friends jumping over the clouds.

How many sheep can you count? Write it here.

BAA BAA
BAA BAA

Show time

Make your own CoComelon puppets and get ready for your own adventures.

It's JJ!

You will need:

Safety scissors

Glue

Thin card

Lolly sticks

Your grown up

fold here

Sweet love

fold here

Let's play!

Instructions:

1. Carefully cut out this page with your grown-up.
2. Stick to thin card and wait to dry.
3. Snip out the friends with your grown-up.
4. Stick the friends to lolly sticks.
5. Have fun, creating your own Cocomelon adventures.

Ask a grown-up for help before using scissors.

Time for bed!

Can you help JJ get ready for bed?

Pretend to do the actions below. Tick off each one when you've done it.

1

Wash your face. Scrub, scrub, scrub!

2

Brush your teeth! It's time to get all clean!

3

Time to put on your pyjamas! Can you wriggle, wriggle, wriggle into them?

4 Get in bed. Snuggle up with your favourite toy.

5 It's story time. Choose your favourite and ask your grown-up to read it for you.

6 You're getting sleepy. Close your eyes and pretend to drift off to sleep. Zzzz.

Night Night

Train song

Let's Sing

clicka Clacka Clicka
I'm on a train

I'm listening to all the sounds
The engine makes

68

And 'neath the train there are some tracks
The train goes Clicka Clacka

Clacka Clicka Clacka

I'm on a train

Can you make the same noise as a train?

Find the friend

Can you spot who is hiding in each group?

Shout out my name when you've found me!

Answers on pages 76-77

Play with me!

Test your memory with this fun game!

Look at the picture for 30 seconds, then cover it up.

a

Yes yes yes!

b

Now look at picture b. One item has been removed, can you spot what it is?

Answers on pages 76-77

Let's paint

Help YoYo paint the toy caterpillar from school.

You will need:
Paints

Old sheet or table cloth

Dishes

Ask a grown-up to help you

Instructions:

1. Protect your table with an old tablecloth.
2. Pour some paint into small dishes.
3. Dip your fingers into the paint and dab onto the circles.
4. Have fun creating a beautiful picture.

Counting Fun!

Count along with us.

1

1 2 3

Hurray!

4

3

I can do anything!

Tick all the things you'd like to do!

- ☐ Go to school
- ☐ Count to 10
- ☐ Make a building block tower
- ☐ Ride a bike
- ☐ Play with friends
- ☐ Visit the moon

Ready for adventure!

Answers

Pages 10-11 Time to Play

JJ's shorts are yellow.
No. TomTom is not in the second picture.

Page 12 Perfect Puzzle

Pages 14-15 I Can See...

Pages 16-17 Scrub, Scrub, Scrub!

Carrots and apples help your teeth stay healthy.

Pages 24-25 Cody's Having a Party

Page 31 Amazing Animals
1 – c, 2 – a, 3 – b, 4 – d

Pages 32-33 It's Bath Time

P57 Happy and Smart!

Pages 52-53 Happy Sunny Day

P70 Find the Friend

JJ is hiding in both rows.

Page 54 Fast Colourful Cars

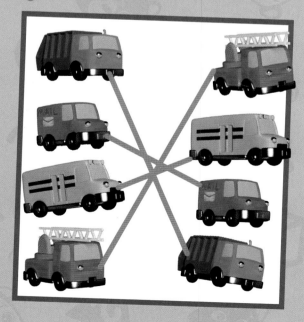

P71 Play with Me!

Jellybean has been removed.